Sammy's
New Food Week

Sammy, Sammy it is time for lunch,
How about some yummy food to munch?
What different foods can we try today?
It's good to try something new, Hooray
Hooray

Monday

What shall we try first; this looks like a tree,
A green stalk, with a green top, yummy broccoli.
Cut it up and take **one** bite at a time,
Well done Sammy, you are doing just fine.

Tuesday

Yummy fresh eggs, shall we have them scrambled or fried?
Or simply boiled with toasted soldiers on one side?

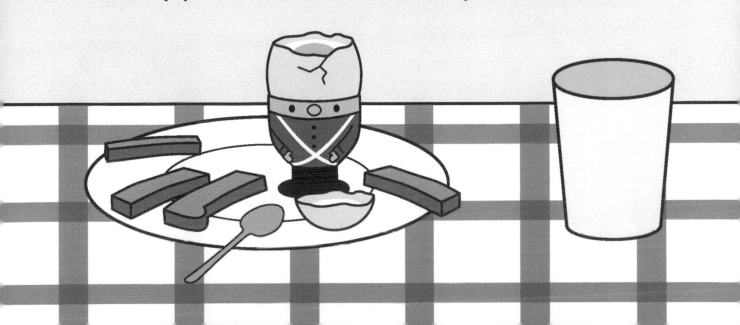

Mummy has taken the top off; the yolk is very yellow,
Sammy you are doing a great job, my little fellow.

Wednesday

At the end of our garden our lovely fruit tree,
Mummy has made a picnic, just for you and me.

Take a bite into your apple; its shiny, red skin,
But don't eat the pips; they will go in the bin.

Thursday

A plate full of spaghetti, go on, give it a try,
Twirl it around on your fork, don't be shy.
How about some sauce, here on your plate?
Sluuurrpppp, I can see a very messy little face.

Friday

Here is some fish on the side of your plate,
Some golden chips too, that looks great.

Would you like some ketchup? Then you could dip,
That lovely fish and that long, crispy, chip.

Try a jacket potato with its crispy skin,
And in the middle put some butter in.
How about some beans with some grated cheese too?
Blow it Sammy, I hope it's not too hot for you?

Mummy's favourite. A roast chicken dinner,
How about you Sammy, is it a winner?
A little in your mouth and carefully chew,
Shall Mummy pour on some gravy for you?

Trying new foods isn't easy I know,
But look how they will help you grow.
You tried something new every single day,
You are my clever little boy, Hooray
Hooray

More
Sammy and Suzie titles

Suzie Goes to a Funeral

Suzie's Toilet Time

Suzie Goes on an Aeroplane

Suzie's Dressing Up Day

Suzie Goes to the Hairdresser

Suzie Goes to School

Sammy Goes on an Aeroplane

Suzie's Christmas Time

Suzie and Cruzie

Visit www.suziebooks.co.uk/index.htm

Lightning Source UK Ltd.
Milton Keynes UK
UKHW022053041221
394987UK00003B/63

9 781910 864623